WORLD OF
VOCABULARY

YELLOW

Sidney J. Rauch

Alfred B. Weinstein

Assisted by Carole Reynolds

Photo Credits

p. 2: Brian Lanker, from his book *I Dream A World*; **p. 5:** Brian Lanker, from his book *I Dream A World*; **p. 8:** the MacNeil/Lehrer News Hour; **p. 10:** New York *Daily News*; **p. 13:** New York *Daily News*; **p. 18:** Tony Costa/Outline; **p. 21:** John Barr/Gamma Liaison; **p. 23:** Smeal/Galella; **p. 26:** © Ruben Guzman; **p. 29:** © Ruben Guzman; **p. 33:** © Ruben Guzman; **p. 34:** Barry Talesnick/Retna Ltd.; **p. 37:** Outline; **p. 39:** Outline; **p. 42:** The Bettmann Archive; **p. 45:** The Bettmann Archive; **p. 47:** The Bettmann Archive; **p. 50:** The *Amsterdam News*; **p. 53:** The *Amsterdam News*; **p. 55:** The *Amsterdam News*; **p. 58:** The Bettmann Archive; **p. 61:** The Bettmann Archive; **p. 63:** The Bettmann Archive; **p. 66:** Popperfoto; **p. 69:** The Granger Collection; **p. 71:** The Granger Collection; **p. 74:** © 1989 Warner Bros. Inc. All rights reserved; **p. 77:** © 1989 Warner Bros. Inc. All rights reserved; **p. 79:** © 1989 Warner Bros. Inc. All rights reserved; **p. 82:** Bernie Liebler; **p. 85:** Bernie Liebler; **p. 87:** John Zimmerman; **p. 90:** Ron Galella; **p. 93:** Globe Photos; **p. 95:** Ron Galella; **p. 98:** Wide World Photos; **p. 101:** Wide World Photos; **p. 103:** Wide World Photos; **p. 106:** UPI/The Bettmann Archive; **p. 109:** N.R. Rowan, Stock Boston; **p. 113:** The Bettmann Archive; **p. 114:** Wide World Photos; **p. 117:** Wide World Photos; **p. 119:** Wide World Photos.

World of Vocabulary, Yellow Level, Third Edition

Sidney J. Rauch • **Alfred B. Weinstein**

Printed in the United States of America

3 4 5 6 7 8 9 10   99 98

ISBN: 0-8359-1279-5

AUTHORS

Sidney J. Rauch is Professor Emeritus of Reading and Education at Hofstra University in Hempstead, New York. He has been a visiting professor at numerous universities (University of Vermont; Appalachian State University, North Carolina; Queens College, New York; The State University at Albany, New York) and is active as an author, consultant, and evaluator. His publications include three textbooks, thirty workbooks, and over 80 professional articles. His *World of Vocabulary* series has sold over two and one-half million copies.

Dr. Rauch has served as consultant and/or evaluator for over thirty school districts in New York, Connecticut, Florida, North Carolina, South Carolina, and the U.S. Virgin Islands. His awards include "Reading Educator of the Year" from the New York State Reading Association (1985); "Outstanding Educator Award" presented by the Colby College Alumni Association (1990); and the College Reading Association Award for "Outstanding Contributions to the Field of Reading" (1991). The *Journal of Reading Education* selected Dr. Rauch's article, "The Balancing Effect Continue: Whole Language Faces Reality" for its "Outstanding Article Award," 1993-1994.

Two of the *Barnaby Brown* books, The Visitor from Outer Space, and *The Return of B.B.* were selected as "Children's Choices" winners for 1991 in a poll conducted by the New York State Reading Association.

Alfred B. Weinstein is the former principal of Myra S. Barnes Intermediate School (Staten Island, N.Y.). Dr. Weinstein has taught extensively at the secondary school level, and he has served as an elementary school principal and assistant principal. He has been a reading clinician and instructor at Hofstra University Reading Center. At Queens College he gave courses in reading improvement, and at Brooklyn College he taught reading for the New York City Board of Education's in-service teacher training program. He was head of Unit 1 of the Board of Examiners and supervised the licensing of teachers, supervisors, administrators, psychologists, and social workers for the New York City Board of Education. He is vice-president of the Council of Supervisors and Administrators of Local 1 of the AFL-CIO. Dr. Weinstein has been listed in *Who's Who in the East* since 1982.

Dr. Weinstein is a contributor to the Handbook for the Volunteer Tutor and one of the authors of Achieving Reading Skills. With Dr. Rauch, he is coauthor of *Mastering Reading Skills*.

CONTENTS

As a young girl, Charlayne Hunter-Gault enjoyed reading a comic strip about a young female reporter named Brenda Starr. Hunter-Gault hoped to one day become a **reporter** like Brenda Starr. She wanted to write about the news.

Years later, Hunter-Gault's dream came true. She worked as a reporter for *The New York Times*. Then she became a newscaster on the "MacNeil/Lehrer News Hour." She received many awards for reporting the news.

But before Hunter-Gault began to work as a news reporter, she was the news. In 1961, she was the first African American female student to go to the ***University*** of Georgia. It was a ***difficult*** time for Hunter-Gault. People yelled at her. They called her names. One night, a brick crashed through her window. She remembers thinking, "Wow! There is a **riot** in my room." But she would not let herself be afraid. She was **confident** that she would one day fulfill her dream. She did not let anything **interfere** with her goals. In 1963, Hunter-Gault graduated with a degree in journalism.

Hunter-Gault brings the same strength to her job as a reporter. She believes it is a reporter's job to tell people the truth. She speaks out against ***injustice*** in the United States and around the world. Hunter-Gault says, "If people are ***informed,*** they will do the right thing."

MAKE A LIST

>>>> *There are eight vocabulary words in this lesson. In the story, they are boxed in color. Copy the vocabulary words here.*

1._____   5._____

2._____   6._____

3._____   7._____

4._____   8._____

>>>> *Here are the eight words you copied on the previous page. Write them in alphabetical order in the spaces below.*

confident	university	difficult	injustice
reporter	informed	interfere	riot

1._____   5._____

2._____   6._____

3._____   7._____

4._____   8._____

WHAT DO THE WORDS MEAN?

>>>> *Following are some meanings, or definitions, for the eight vocabulary words in this lesson. Write the words next to their definitions.*

1._____ having faith or trust in oneself

2._____ someone who writes about or tells about the news

3._____ something that harms the rights of others

4._____ not easy; hard

5._____ given information; told

6._____ a school of higher learning; college

7._____ a wild disturbance caused by a group of people

8._____ to get in the way of

4

USE YOUR OWN WORDS

>>>> *Look at the picture. What words come into your mind? Write them on the lines below. To help you get started, here are two good words:*

1._____smart_____   5._____

2._____determined_____   6._____

3._____   7._____

4._____   8._____

>>>> A **synonym** is a word that means the same, or nearly the same, as another word. *Happy* and *glad* are synonyms.

>>>> *The column on the left contains the eight key words in the story. To the right of each key word are three other words or groups of words. Two of these are synonyms for the key word. Circle the two synonyms.*

1.	**difficult**	easy	hard	not easy
2.	**interfere**	block	interrupt	interest
3.	**riot**	violence	disturbance	playfulness
4.	**university**	school	park	college
5.	**reporter**	writer	news gatherer	newspaper
6.	**confident**	secure	sure	uncertain
7.	**informed**	told	given information	questioned
8.	**injustice**	injury	unfairness	uniform

>>>> *In each of the following sentences, there are words that need capital letters. Rewrite each sentence so that the words are correctly capitalized. Remember that capital letters are used in the following places: first word in a sentence; names of people, cities, states, countries; days of the week; months of the year.*

1. charlayne hunter-gault was born in south carolina on february 27, 1942.

_____

_____

2. in 1961, charlayne hunter-gault was a student at the university of georgia.

_____

_____

_____

3. she and hamilton holmes were the first african american students at this athens, georgia, school.

_____

_____

_____

4. she worked for the *new yorker* and *the new york times*.

_____

_____

5. hunter-gault's report on troubles in south africa won the george foster peabody award.

_____

_____

>>>> *Here are the eight vocabulary words for this lesson:*

confident	university	difficult	injustice
reporter	informed	interfere	riot

>>>> *There are four blank spaces in the story below. Four vocabulary words have already been used in the story. They are underlined. Use the other four words to fill in the blanks.*

One day Charlayne Hunter-Gault was _____ that she was going to a new school. She would be the first African American female student there. Hunter-Gault knew she would have a <u>difficult</u> time. Some people did not want her at the _____. They tried to <u>interfere</u> in many ways. They thought that a _____ would frighten the new student. But Hunter-Gault was <u>confident</u>. She did not let this _____ keep her from her dream. She was going to learn to be a <u>reporter</u>. Hunter-Gault would not let this dream slip away.

>>>> *On a separate sheet of paper or in your notebook or journal, complete one or more of the activities below.*

Building Language

Listen to a radio or a television newscast. Write down the words you do not understand. Write what you think each word might mean as it was used. Then look each word up in a dictionary and see how close you came to understanding its meaning.

Learning Across the Curriculum

In 1954, the Supreme Court ruled that separate schools for African Americans and whites were unconstitutional. Seven years later, this landmark decision helped Charlayne Hunter-Gault enter the University of Georgia. Visit the library to learn more about this Supreme Court decision called *Brown vs. the Board of Education of Topeka, Kansas*. Report your findings to your class.

Broadening Your Understanding

Charlayne Hunter-Gault had the courage to follow her dream at the University of Georgia even though some people tried to stop her. Write a journal entry in which you give your opinion and ideas on what you think it would be like to be in Hunter-Gault's situation. Share your ideas with a classmate if you wish.

The rider settled his boots into the stirrups. He grabbed the rope with his left hand. "Let 'em rip!" he yelled. The gray horse exploded out of the chute. It leaped high into the air. It landed stiff legged. The rider was **jarred.** He held on tightly to the reins. His feet came loose from the stirrups. The horse twisted, spun, and **reared.** It couldn't shake the rider out of the **saddle.** Ten seconds passed. The cowhand had stayed on past the time limit.

This event is part of a **rodeo.** A rodeo is a show in which cowhands **perform** acts of horsemanship and roping. *Rodeo* means "roundup" in Spanish. In the old days, the ranch hands held contests to test their skills. Wild horses had to be broken for ranch work. Cowhands had to use horses and ropes to help **brand** the cattle. These tests of skills became part of the **modern** rodeo.

A rodeo is made up of five main events. One is saddle riding, or bronco busting. The other four are bareback riding, steer wrestling, calf roping, and bull riding.

The riding and roping events are dangerous. Torn muscles, chipped teeth, and broken bones are common. Yet, in spite of these dangers, rodeo performers seldom quit. They only give up when **injury** or old age makes it impossible to continue.

MAKE A LIST

>>>> *There are eight vocabulary words in this lesson. In the story, they are boxed in color. Copy the vocabulary words here.*

1. _____   5. _____

2. _____   6. _____

3. _____   7. _____

4. _____   8. _____

11

>>>> *Here are the eight words you copied on the previous page. Write them in alphabetical order in the spaces below.*

injury	jarred	saddle	modern
reared	rodeo	brand	perform

1._____   5._____

2._____   6._____

3._____   7._____

4._____   8._____

WHAT DO THE WORDS MEAN?

>>>> *Following are some meanings, or definitions, for the eight vocabulary words in this lesson. Write the words next to their definitions.*

1. _____ leather seat for a rider on horseback

2. _____ new; up-to-date

3. _____ to do; to act

4. _____ a public show for the skills of cowboys and cowgirls

5. _____ shaken; jolted

6. _____ stood on hind legs; usually done by a horse

7. _____ a wound or damage

8. _____ to make a mark on the skin with a hot iron

USE YOUR OWN WORDS

>>>> *Look at the picture. What words come into your mind? Write them on the lines below. To help you get started, here are two good words:*

1. _____rider_____   5. _____

2. _____bull_____   6. _____

3. _____   7. _____

4. _____   8. _____

>>>> A **synonym** is a word that means the same, or nearly the same, as another word. *Happy* and *glad* are synonyms.

>>>> *The column on the left contains the eight key words in the story. To the right of each key word are three other words or groups of words. Two of these are synonyms for the key word. Circle the two synonyms.*

1.	**jarred**	shaken	jolted	rode
2.	**rodeo**	circus	show	roundup
3.	**brand**	to make a mark	to make fun of	to make a sign
4.	**saddle**	seat	place for rider	seat at rodeo
5.	**perform**	to act	to do	to lie
6.	**injury**	heart	harm	damage
7.	**modern**	old	new	up-to-date
8.	**reared**	stood on hind legs	afraid to move	had front legs off the ground

>>>> *In each of the following sentences, there are words that need capital letters. Rewrite each sentence so the words are correctly capitalized. Remember that capital letters are used in the following places: first word in a sentence; names of people, events, cities, states, countries, and other places; days of the week; and months of the year.*

1. casey tibbs and jim shoulders have both appeared at frontier days.

   Casey Tibbs and Jim Shoulders have both appeared

   at Frontier Days.

2. we have two tickets for the rodeo at madison square garden on april 4.

   _____

   _____

3. angela is the best calf roper at the rocky ranch.

   _____

   _____

4. among the stars who may appear at the pendleton roundup are tanya tucker and willie nelson.

   _____

   _____

5. the bucking horse in the corral belongs to amy and jenny clarke from winding hills, south dakota.

   _____

   _____

>>>> *Here are the eight vocabulary words for this lesson:*

brand	modern	rodeo	perform
saddle	jarred	injury	reared

>>>> *There are four blank spaces in the story below. Four vocabulary words have already been used in the story. They are underlined. Use the other four words to fill in the blanks.*

For many people, the days of the cowhands ended years ago. The ranges got smaller. There were fewer cattle to <u>brand</u> with hot irons. The _____ cowhand seemed to be spending more time in a pickup truck than on a bucking bronco. But for a few weeks a year, the Old West returned. That's when the <u>rodeo</u> came to town.

The cowhands paraded through town. The leader sat proudly in a <u>saddle</u>. The crowd cheered as the riders got ready to _____. Then the contests were on. A wild mustang twisted and _____. The crowd roared. The rider received an <u>injury</u>, but he held on. No matter how much his horse _____ him, the rider wanted to stay on for at least ten seconds. He made it. For a moment, the good old days of the Wild West had returned.

>>>> *On a separate piece of paper or in your notebook or journal, complete one or more of the activities below.*

Building Language

The word *rodeo* comes from Spanish. Make a list of words that come from another language and are now part of English. Write what each word means in its original language. Then write what the word means in English. Use a dictionary if you need help.

Learning Across the Curriculum

Rodeos have been part of United States culture for more than a hundred years. Research the history of rodeos in this country. Write a report about what you find. You may want to illustrate your report with drawings or photographs.

Broadening Your Understanding

Did you know that there are women rodeo stars? Read a book about a woman rodeo star, such as Sammy Fancher Thurman or Annie Oakley. Then write a paragraph about her and share it with your classmates.

Arnold Schwarzenegger was a teenager in Austria who wanted to try out for a *local* soccer team. So he lifted weights. He soon forgot about soccer and became dedicated to weight lifting. He entered several bodybuilding contests and won them all, including the Mr. Universe title five times and Mr. Olympia seven times. "I was *driven* and ambitious," he says. "There was no place to go but America."

He worked hard to develop his body. Luckily for Schwarzenegger, a book and later a movie called *Pumping Iron* made him famous. Schwarzenegger enjoyed working on the movie. He decided he wanted to become a *serious* actor. He gave up bodybuilding competitions. He *approached* his new goal with the same determination he had given weight lifting.

Reviewers were *critical* of his early movies. Yet, Schwarzenegger did not give up. He worked to improve his acting skills. He continued to make movies. His *Terminator* movie was very popular with fans. It made a lot of money. Finally, Schwarzenegger was a major motion picture star! His *wit,* dedication, and ambition had won him many fans. Throughout his life, Arnold Schwarzenegger has *demonstrated* that you are what you believe you can be.

MAKE A LIST

>>>> *There are eight vocabulary words in this lesson. In the story, they are boxed in color. Copy the vocabulary words here.*

1._____   5._____

2._____   6._____

3._____   7._____

4._____   8._____

MAKE AN ALPHABETICAL LIST

>>>> *Here are the eight words you copied on the previous page. Write them in alphabetical order in the spaces below.*

local	serious	driven	approached
critical	demonstrated	wit	reviewers

1. _____

2. _____

3. _____

4. _____

5. _____

6. _____

7. _____

8. _____

WHAT DO THE WORDS MEAN?

>>>> *Following are some meanings, or definitions, for the eight vocabulary words in this lesson. Write the words next to their definitions.*

1. _____ people who tell about new films

2. _____ humor; intelligence

3. _____ of a small area; regional

4. _____ showed; proved

5. _____ sober; sincere

6. _____ ambitious; filled with the need to succeed

7. _____ disapproving; not supportive

8. _____ worked on; moved toward

USE YOUR OWN WORDS

>>>> *Look at the picture. What words come into your mind? Write them on the lines below. To help you get started, here are two good words:*

1. ___powerful___

2. ___movie star___

3. _____

4. _____

5. _____

6. _____

7. _____

8. _____

>>>> A **synonym** is a word that means the same, or nearly the same, as another word. *Happy* and *glad* are synonyms.

>>>> *The column on the left contains the eight key words in the story. To the right of each key word are three other words or groups of words. Two of these are synonyms for the key word. Circle the two synonyms.*

1. **wit**	foolish	humor	intelligence
2. **driven**	determined	failed	worked toward a goal
3. **serious**	somber	joking	grave
4. **critical**	unkind	not approving	not judging
5. **reviewers**	critics	fans	judges
6. **local**	national	regional	of a small area
7. **approached**	went away from	moved toward	worked on
8. **demonstrated**	showed	gave proof	sold

>>>> The **subject** of a sentence tells what is being talked or written about. It can be one word or a group of words. The underlined words in these sentences are subjects.

Arnold lifted weights as a teenager.
He became very interested in bodybuilding.

>>>> *Underline the subjects in the following sentences.*

1. An actor has to be more than handsome.

2. Many skills make a good actor.

3. Movies require timing and talent.

4. Arnold works hard to improve his acting skills.

5. Thousands of fans see his movies.

6. Many movie producers want Schwarzenegger for their films.

7. A star like Arnold can make a movie a box-office hit.

8. His goal of becoming an actor has been achieved!

Here are the eight vocabulary words for this lesson:

reviewers	approached	driven	wit
demonstrated	serious	critical	local

>>>> *There are four blank spaces in the story below. Four vocabulary words have already been used in the story. They are underlined. Use the other four vocabulary words to fill in the blanks.*

It is not always easy to become a <u>serious</u> actor. You may have been very successful in _____ events, but that doesn't mean you will have fans all over the country. Also <u>reviewers</u> can be harmful. If their remarks are _____, your career can come to a full stop.

If you are still _____ to become famous, here are some tips. You must have <u>demonstrated</u> some talent that people will admire. You should also have a quick and unforgettable _____. Fans like to repeat what you have said. People who have <u>approached</u> acting with these traits have become great stars!

On a separate sheet of paper or in your notebook or journal, complete one or more of the activities below.

Broadening Your Understanding

Throughout his career, Arnold Schwarzenegger has been involved with Special Olympics. Research this program to discover its origins and goals. Find out how a person in your community could help with the event. Share your information with the class.

Learning Across the Curriculum

Bodybuilders are very careful to eat certain types of foods while in training. All people should eat foods from each of the different food groups to keep their bodies healthy. Find out more about the basic food groups and the number of servings a person your age should eat from each group. Make a poster displaying this information for your class.

Learning Across the Curriculum

How exactly do muscles work? Find out and prepare an oral report for your class. You may want to use diagrams or a model to explain what you learn.

A group of young people sat talking. They were students in a **special** writing class. Sandra Cisneros listened. The students talked about their childhoods. They talked about **fancy** schools and homes. Cisneros **remained** silent. She did not want to talk about her childhood. Her family had moved often. They had lived in Mexico. They had lived in a poor part of Chicago. Cisneros was ashamed. She did not want to talk about the **simple** homes her family had lived in.

Cisneros wondered if she should be in the class. She was **quite** different from her classmates. Suddenly, Cisneros was **struck** with an idea. She could write about things her classmates did not know. She could write about life as a Mexican American. Maybe it was good to be different!

Cisneros's first book was *The House on Mango Street*. It is the story of a Mexican American girl. The girl wishes for a better place to live. Much of the story was **based** on Cisneros's own life. The book was a great hit!

Today Cisneros **continues** to write. Her stories are about Spanish-speaking people. In these stories, Cisneros hopes to teach people about life as a Chicano. She hopes that her books help people to think about Chicanos and other Latinos in a new way. She wants to show that it is good to be different.

MAKE A LIST

>>>> *There are eight vocabulary words in this lesson. In the story, they are in bold type. Copy the vocabulary words here.*

1._____   5._____

2._____   6._____

3._____   7._____

4._____   8._____

MAKE AN ALPHABETICAL LIST

>>>> *Here are the eight words you copied on the previous page. Write them in alphabetical order in the spaces below.*

remained	continues	quite	fancy
struck	special	simple	based

1. _____

2. _____

3. _____

4. _____

5. _____

6. _____

7. _____

8. _____

WHAT DO THE WORDS MEAN?

>>>> *Following are some meanings, or definitions, for the eight vocabulary words in this lesson. Write the words next to their definitions.*

1. _____ continued without change

2. _____ fine; elegant

3. _____ hit with a sudden discovery

4. _____ plain; common

5. _____ centered

6. _____ very

7. _____ different; important

8. _____ goes on

USE YOUR OWN WORDS

>>>> *Look at the picture. What words come into your mind? Write them on the lines below. To help you get started, here are two good words:*

1.   friendly   5. _____

2.   Chicano   6. _____

3. _____ 7. _____

4. _____ 8. _____

>>>> A **synonym** is a word that means the same, or nearly the same, as another word. *Happy* and *glad* are synonyms.

>>>> *The column on the left contains the eight key words in the story. To the right of each key word are three other words or groups of words. Two of these are synonyms for the key word. Circle the two synonyms.*

1.	**remained**	began	stayed	kept
2.	**continues**	stops	goes on	lasts
3.	**quite**	extremely	very	quickly
4.	**fancy**	dull	fine	elegant
5.	**struck**	hit	hurt	realize
6.	**special**	different	unusual	common
7.	**simple**	not rich	odd	plain
8.	**based**	was mainly about	centered	forgot

>>>> Many words end in *ed, er,* or *ing.* These endings can change the meaning of a word or form a new word.

>>>> *Add the right ending to the word before each sentence. Then write the new word in the blank space. Remember that you sometimes drop the final* e *before adding the ending.*

1. **listen**   Sandra Cisneros _____ to her classmates.

2. **talk**   They were _____ about their childhoods.

3. **remain**   Cisneros _____ silent.

4. **live**   Her family had _____ in simple homes.

5. **move**   She had spent her childhood _____ to Mexico and Chicago.

6. **decide**   Cisneros _____ she was quite different.

7. **write**   She could be a different kind of _____ .

8. **enjoy**   Many people _____ her first novel *The House on Mango Street.*

>>>> *Here are the eight vocabulary words for this lesson:*

fancy	special	simple	remained
struck	quite	continues	based

>>>> *There are four blank spaces in the story below. Four vocabulary words have already been used in the story. They are underlined. Use the other four words to fill in the blanks.*

Sandra Cisneros always wanted to be a writer. After college, she went to a _____ writer's workshop. Cisneros was _____ different from her classmates. They had lived in <u>fancy</u> houses. They had gone to good schools. Cisneros's childhood had been very <u>simple</u>.

Cisneros wondered if she belonged in the class. She could not write like the others. She was different! Cisneros was <u>struck</u> with the idea that it was good to be different. Her stories would be unlike her classmates'. Her stories would be _____ on her life as a Mexican American. Cisneros <u>remained</u> in the class. She wrote stories about Spanish-speaking Americans. Cisneros _____ to write Latino stories today.

>>>> *On a separate sheet of paper or in your notebook or journal, complete one or more of the activities below.*

Broadening Your Understanding

Suppose you were able to interview Sandra Cisneros for a local newspaper. What would you ask her? Think of five questions you would ask this author. Tell them to a partner.

Broadening Your Understanding

Every person is different in some way. Make a list of the ways you differ from your classmates. Use the list to create a story about a "different" kind of person. Share the stories with your classmates.

Learning Across the Curriculum

Research the *La Causa* movement, or *El Movimiento*, which was a movement to give full rights to Mexican Americans. Find out how the movement helped both Americans and Mexicans.

For many young children, performing with famous musicians is simply a pretend game. But for Terri Lyne Carrington, everyday life was like a pretend game. Terri Lyne Carrington grew up in the *presence* of famous musicians. Her family had a *connection* to *quality* jazz. Matt Carrington, her grandfather, played with jazz greats Fats Waller and Chuck Berry. As a result, Carrington was *literally* raised on jazz.

At the age of 7, Carrington began a career as a drummer. She was only 10 when she played with pianist Oscar Peterson and trumpeter Dizzy Gillespie. Exciting as the life was, Carrington admits, "I didn't know I was doing anything extraordinary. To me, they were all just normal people."

Her early connections with jazz paid off as she got older. She landed a job as drummer with the otherwise all-male band of the "Arsenio Hall Show" on television. She got the job by being extraordinary herself. The band's director says, "She had what all the others had plus her own *essence.* She can pull out at any moment some *staggering* *display.*" Carrington is more modest. "I was able to grow and develop each night," she says. Now that the show is off the air, Carrington faces an exciting future traveling to the *beat* of her own drum.

MAKE A LIST

>>>> *There are eight vocabulary words in this lesson. In the story, they are boxed in color. Copy the vocabulary words here.*

1._____   5._____

2._____   6._____

3._____   7._____

4._____   8._____

MAKE AN ALPHABETICAL LIST

>>>> *Here are the eight words you copied on the previous page. Write them in alphabetical order in the spaces below.*

connection	essence	quality	staggering
literally	display	presence	beat

1._____   5._____

2._____   6._____

3._____   7._____

4._____   8._____

WHAT DO THE WORDS MEAN?

>>>> *Following are some meanings, or definitions, for the eight vocabulary words in this lesson. Write the words next to their definitions.*

1. _____ overwhelming

2. _____ a demonstration

3. _____ in the company of

4. _____ actually

5. _____ basic character

6. _____ of obvious excellence

7. _____ the rhythm of a piece of music

8. _____ a link

USE YOUR OWN WORDS

>>>> *Look at the picture. What words come into your mind? Write them on the lines below. To help you get started, here are two good words:*

1._____talented_____   5._____

2._____musician_____   6._____

3._____   7._____

4._____   8._____

37

>>>> A **synonym** is a word that means the same, or nearly the same, as another word. *Happy* and *glad* are synonyms.

>>>> *The column on the left contains the eight key words in the story. To the right of each key word are three other words or groups of words. Two of these are synonyms for the key word. Circle the two synonyms.*

1.	**presence**	company	gifts	in the sight of
2.	**display**	show	opening	performance
3.	**quality**	excellent	fine	amount
4.	**staggering**	terrible	unexpected	amazing
5.	**essence**	core	goodness	base
6.	**literally**	slowly	truly	exactly
7.	**beat**	musical pulse	mix	rhythm
8.	**connection**	attachment	link	change

>>>> **Verbs** are words that express action or being. The underlined words in these sentences are verbs.

Go to the concert.
Carrington is a great drummer.
Can she play any other instrument?

>>>> *Underline the verbs in the following sentences.*

1. Terri Lyne Carrington played at the age of 5.

2. She has performed with many jazz greats.

3. Did you see her on the "Arsenio Hall Show"?

4. She performed brilliantly and enjoyed the show.

5. Who is the leader of that band?

6. Everyone likes the music.

7. Carrington always has had a special quality.

8. She almost did not try the drums.

COMPLETE THE STORY

>>>> *Here are the eight vocabulary words for this lesson:*

connection	essence	quality	staggering
literally	display	presence	beat

>>>> *There are four blank spaces in the story below. Four vocabulary words have already been used in the story. They are underlined. Use the other four words to fill in the blanks.*

Terri Lyne Carrington grew up in the _____ of many great musicians. Her first <u>connection</u> to jazz was through her grandfather. He played with some famous musicians. Carrington showed great talent when she was only 5 years old. Her talent was on _____ in concerts before she was 10. Her skill was <u>staggering</u> to many people who expected undeveloped talent.

Jazz has <u>literally</u> given her life its direction. She even won a scholarship at the age of 11. She plays _____ music in every band she joins. Her drums set the _____ for the other players. Yet, all of her performances somehow capture the <u>essence</u> of this remarkable young woman. Hers is a career to watch!

>>>> *On a separate sheet of paper or in your notebook or journal, complete one or more of the activities below.*

Working Together

Listen to a jazz recording with a group. Have every person write a description of what he or she hears. Use words that make you think of the music. Then have everyone read aloud his or her description. Combine the descriptions into one that would best explain the music to someone who has never heard it.

Learning Across the Curriculum

Find out more about jazz. Ask your librarian for help. Discover what sets it apart from other kinds of music, such as country or rock-and-roll. Make a poster for the class that shows the type of instruments commonly found in a jazz ensemble.

Appreciating Diversity

Although jazz was born in the United States, every other country has its own musical traditions. Choose a country and research its musical heritage. Then give an oral report. If you can, play some music.

6 MOUNTAIN OF ICE

The *Titanic* was supposed to be one of the safest ships in the world. On April 14, 1912, the *Titanic* was crossing the Atlantic Ocean. The night was foggy, but the passengers were not worried. Suddenly, there was a **horrible** noise. The *Titanic* had hit an **iceberg**! At 2:05 A.M. the *Titanic* sank. More than 1,500 people drowned.

An iceberg is an **immense** piece of ice that floats in the ocean. *Berg* is the German word for "mountain." So *iceberg* means "mountain of ice." Icebergs are dangerous because they are so big. But only a very small part of an iceberg is **visible.** The rest of the iceberg is **beneath** the surface of the water.

Icebergs are really the snows of hundreds or thousands of years ago. Icebergs start as snowfall in Greenland. Because it is so cold there, very little snow melts. As more snow falls, the snow becomes thick and hard. The bottom turns to ice. This ice, moving slowly toward the sea, is called a **glacier.** When a **chunk** of the glacier falls into the sea, it is called an iceberg. An iceberg is moved south by wind and ocean currents. If it floats far enough south, a ship may run into the iceberg. This happened to the *Titanic*.

The International Ice Patrol was **established** soon after the sinking of the *Titanic*. Since that time, no ships have been lost because of icebergs.

MAKE A LIST

>>>> *There are eight vocabulary words in this lesson. In the story, they are boxed in color. Copy the vocabulary words here.*

1. _____   5. _____

2. _____   6. _____

3. _____   7. _____

4. _____   8. _____

MAKE AN ALPHABETICAL LIST

>>>> *Here are the eight words you copied on the previous page. Write them in alphabetical order in the spaces below.*

immense	beneath	chunk	horrible
glacier	established	visible	iceberg

1. _____   5. _____

2. _____   6. _____

3. _____   7. _____

4. _____   8. _____

WHAT DO THE WORDS MEAN?

>>>> *Following are some meanings, or definitions, for the eight vocabulary words in this lesson. Write the words next to their definitions.*

1. _____ a short, thick piece; good-size portion

2. _____ able to be seen or observed

3. _____ a mountain of ice; a large chunk of ice broken off from a glacier

4. _____ below; underneath

5. _____ terrible; frightful

6. _____ set up; founded

7. _____ huge; very large

8. _____ an extremely large mass of ice and snow

USE YOUR OWN WORDS

>>>> *Look at the picture. What words come into your mind? Write them on the lines below. To help you get started, here are two good words:*

1.   panic   5. _____

2.   crowd   6. _____

3. _____ 7. _____

4. _____ 8. _____

>>>> A **synonym** is a word that means the same, or nearly the same, as another word. *Happy* and *glad* are synonyms.

>>>> *The column on the left contains the eight key words in the story. To the right of each key word are three other words or groups of words. Two of these are synonyms for the key word. Circle the two synonyms.*

1. **immense**	moving	very large	huge
2. **chunk**	piece	part	smooth
3. **glacier**	mass of ice	mountain	huge amount of moving snow
4. **visible**	can be moved	can be seen	can be spotted
5. **established**	destroyed	set up	organized
6. **iceberg**	mountain of ice	melted ice	huge chunk of ice
7. **horrible**	terrible	noisy	very bad
8. **beneath**	below	underneath	beside

>>>>A **contraction** is a short form of a word or a word group. For example, *can't* is a contraction of *cannot*. *I'll* is a contraction of *I will*. Contractions are formed by putting an apostrophe (') in place of the missing letter or letters.

>>>> *Write the contractions for the underlined words.*

1. We asked Bob to come with us, but he <u>had not</u> finished his homework. _____

2. <u>We are</u> planning to move to Chicago next month. _____

3. <u>I am</u> not looking forward to going. _____

4. <u>She will</u> talk about glaciers every chance she gets. _____

5. Marsha said that <u>you have</u> actually seen an iceberg. _____

6. Did you ask <u>who is</u> coming to the party? _____

Here are the eight vocabulary words for this lesson:

glacier	visible	beneath	established
chunk	immense	iceberg	horrible

>>>> **There are four blank spaces in the story below. Four vocabulary words have already been used in the story. They are underlined. Use the other four words to fill in the blanks.**

Our ship is moving slowly through icy waters. We have been warned about an <u>iceberg</u>. We know that icebergs are dangerous. Only a small part of the mountain of ice is _____. The rest is hidden <u>beneath</u> the surface of the sea. We are on the lookout for an <u>immense</u> _____ of ice. We do not want to repeat the lesson of the *Titanic*. That _____ accident will never leave our minds. More than 1,500 people died because a great ship hit an iceberg. Many new safety rules had to be _____ because of the *Titanic*.

Since April 1912, no ship has sunk because of an iceberg. The U.S. Coast Guard and the International Ice Patrol watch carefully. They know that an iceberg breaks off from a <u>glacier</u>. They watch these slow-moving masses of ice and warn all nearby ships.

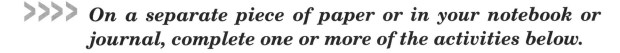

>>>> *On a separate piece of paper or in your notebook or journal, complete one or more of the activities below.*

Broadening Your Understanding

In 1986, researchers explored the underwater wreck of the *Titanic* in a three-person submarine. Research what they discovered. Then write several diary entries as if you were part of the exploration team and were recording your adventure.

Learning Across the Curriculum

Using a songbook from the library find the words to the song "The Titanic." If possible, listen to a recording of the song. Then write how close the song comes to telling what really happened on the *Titanic*.

Extending Your Reading

When divers brought up the artifacts that had been on the *Titanic*, everyone wanted to know what they had found. People have always been interested in sunken ships. Read one of the books listed below. Then present a report to the class about the most interesting sunken treasure story you read.

Shipwrecks: Terror and Treasure, by Kathryn Lon Humphrey
Missing Treasures, by Caroline Evensen Lazo
Tales of Hidden Treasure, by Alvin Schwartz
Exploring the Titanic, by Robert Ballad

7 SEARCHING FOR ROOTS

Alex Haley had a strong *desire.* He wanted to know where his family came from. He searched for 12 years. He *traced* his family back to Africa. He met a storyteller in Gambia on the west coast of Africa. The storyteller told Haley about his great-great-grandfather Kunta Kinte. Haley learned how Kinte was caught by slavers. He was chained and thrown into the hold of a slave ship. Life on board was horrible.

Haley studied the history of Kinte and his *descendants* in America. He wrote their story in his book *Roots*. It became a bestseller. Haley became famous. Later, a short television *series* based on the book ran for eight nights. It *attracted* an audience of millions. Americans saw how slaves were treated. They had no rights. They were cruelly *separated* from their families. Their masters treated them harshly. The book and the series showed how Kinte and his descendants fought to become free.

Haley believed that all of us are searching for our roots. He thought that we should get to know our families and their histories better. Then we will *discover* things about our past that we might never have known. Haley never gave up searching for his roots. His *ancestor* Kinte never gave up his search for freedom.

MAKE A LIST

>>>> *There are eight vocabulary words in this lesson. In the story, they are boxed in color. Copy the vocabulary words here.*

1._____   5._____

2._____   6._____

3._____   7._____

4._____   8._____

MAKE AN ALPHABETICAL LIST

>>>> *Here are the eight words you copied on the previous page. Write them in alphabetical order in the spaces below.*

series	ancestor	discover	separated
attracted	traced	desire	descendants

1._____   5._____

2._____   6._____

3._____   7._____

4._____   8._____

WHAT DO THE WORDS MEAN?

>>>> *Following are some meanings, or definitions, for the eight vocabulary words in this lesson. Write the words next to their definitions.*

1. _____   television show that appears each week

2. _____   apart; not together

3. _____   followed; tracked

4. _____   to find out; to uncover

5. _____   people born of a certain family; heirs

6. _____   gathered; brought together

7. _____   wish; purpose

8. _____   great-grandparent or one who came before; heirs

USE YOUR OWN WORDS

>>>> *Look at the picture. What words come into your mind? Write them on the lines below. To help you get started, here are two good words:*

1. _____hats_____   5. _____

2. _____characters_____   6. _____

3. _____   7. _____

4. _____   8. _____

FIND THE SYNONYMS

>>>> A **synonym** is a word that means the same, or nearly the same, as another word. *Happy* and *glad* are synonyms.

>>>> *The column on the left contains the eight key words in the story. To the right of each key word are three other words or groups of words. Two of these are synonyms for the key word. Circle the two synonyms.*

1. **attracted**	brought together	separated	gathered
2. **traced**	located	tracked down	wrote about
3. **descendants**	heirs	fighters	children
4. **desire**	wish	intention	hatred
5. **separated**	set apart	attracted	scattered
6. **series**	items in a row	breakfast food	weekly TV show
7. **ancestor**	great-grandmother	children	great-grandfather
8. **discover**	uncover	find out	leave

>>>> *These five sentences have been scrambled or mixed up. Write the words in the correct order so that they make complete sentences.*

1. book called Alex *Roots* a Haley wrote

   Alex Haley wrote a book called *Roots*.

2. West is country in Gambia a Africa

3. America people to from countries many other come

4. grandparents to Italy moved my Chicago from

5. Cicely *Roots* of stars one Tyson was the of

>>>> **Here are the eight vocabulary words for this lesson:**

series	attracted	ancestor	traced
discover	desire	separated	descendants

>>>> *There are four blank spaces in the story below. Four vocabulary words have already been used in the story. They are underlined. Use the other four words to fill in the blanks.*

Almost anyone can <u>discover</u> his or her roots. Alex Haley _____ his roots back to Africa. His _____ Kunta Kinte had come from West Africa. He was <u>separated</u> from his family and sold as a slave. Kunta Kinte's _____ found out about their past through Haley's research. They and millions of other people read Haley's book or watched the television <u>series</u>. Many North Americans are _____ to the idea of finding out where they came from. It is a strong <u>desire</u> that many of us share.

>>>> *On a separate piece of paper or in your notebook or journal, complete one or more of the activities below.*

Learning Across the Curriculum

Interview people in your family to discover something about your heritage. Find out what countries your parents or ancestors came from. Write a short history of your family with the information you find out.

Broadening Your Understanding

Interview people in your class to find out where all their ancestors were born. Make a list of all the countries. Put pins on a world map to show what you have learned.

Learning Across the Curriculum

The history of a community is based on all the people who have lived there. Go to your library or local historical society. Find out what groups of people have been in your community and when. Report what you find to the class.

58

Would you like to know your future? Many would jump at the **opportunity** to find out what will happen to them. Some people go to astrologers. These people study the **planets** to tell the future.

Astrologers need to know the exact time and place of your birth. They then make up a **chart** of the heavens. It shows where the sun and moon were at the time of your birth. It also shows where the other planets were.

Astrologers divide the heavens into 12 equal parts. Each part is named after a group of stars. The starting group is Aries, the Ram. Taurus, the Bull, is next. Ten other groups, or signs, follow. The names of the signs came from an **ancient** people.

Astrologers believe that people behave the way they do because of their signs. For example, those born under the sign of Aries are **ambitious.** They want to get ahead. Those born under the sign of Leo are said to be **generous.** They are willing to share.

Scientists believe that astrology is nonsense. They think it is based on **superstition.** They say that we act the way we do because of our parents. The way we are raised is important. Scientists do not believe that the position of the stars or planets at the time of birth decides our **future.** What do you think?

MAKE A LIST

>>>> *There are eight vocabulary words in this lesson. In the story, they are boxed in color. Copy the vocabulary words here.*

1. _____   5. _____
2. _____   6. _____
3. _____   7. _____
4. _____   8. _____

MAKE AN ALPHABETICAL LIST

>>>> *Here are the eight words you copied on the previous page. Write them in alphabetical order in the spaces below.*

opportunity	chart	planets	superstition
generous	future	ancient	ambitious

1. _____   5. _____

2. _____   6. _____

3. _____   7. _____

4. _____   8. _____

WHAT DO THE WORDS MEAN?

>>>> *Following are some meanings, or definitions, for the eight vocabulary words in this lesson. Write the words next to their definitions.*

1. _____ a time to come; time that is ahead

2. _____ willing to share

3. _____ a chance, usually a good one

4. _____ the nine heavenly bodies that orbit the sun

5. _____ belief based on ignorance and fear

6. _____ wanting fame or success

7. _____ a diagram; a map; a graph

8. _____ belonging to times long past; very old

USE YOUR OWN WORDS

>>>> *Look at the picture. What words come into your mind? Write them on the lines below. To help you get started, here are two good words:*

1. _____stars_____

2. ____old-fashioned____

3. _____

4. _____

5. _____

6. _____

7. _____

8. _____

>>>> A **synonym** is a word that means the same, or nearly the same, as another word. *Happy* and *glad* are synonyms.

>>>> *The column on the left contains the eight key words in the story. To the right of each key word are three other words or groups of words. Two of these are synonyms for the key word. Circle the two synonyms.*

1. **chart**	ship	map	diagram
2. **future**	what is ahead	what is past	a time to come
3. **opportunity**	faith	chance	possibility
4. **superstition**	belief based on fear	science	false idea
5. **generous**	unselfish	rich	caring
6. **ancient**	old	aged	mysterious
7. **planets**	heavenly bodies	sun orbiters	moons
8. **ambitious**	seeking quiet	seeking fame	wanting success

>>>> Some words are often confused because they look alike or sound alike. For example, *there/their* and *where/wear* are often confused.

>>>> **Place the correct word in the blank spaces in the following sentences.**

1. **(red, read)** I think I'll have my palm _____ by a fortuneteller.

2. **(pair, pear)** The fruit Cynthia likes best is a _____.

3. **(cents, sense)** I have more _____ than to believe in astrology.

4. **(stare, stair)** Clara was so surprised that all she could do was _____.

5. **(stake, steak)** When you put up the tent, make sure each _____ is firmly in the ground.

6. **(bare, bear)** When we go to the zoo, Katie likes to visit her favorite _____.

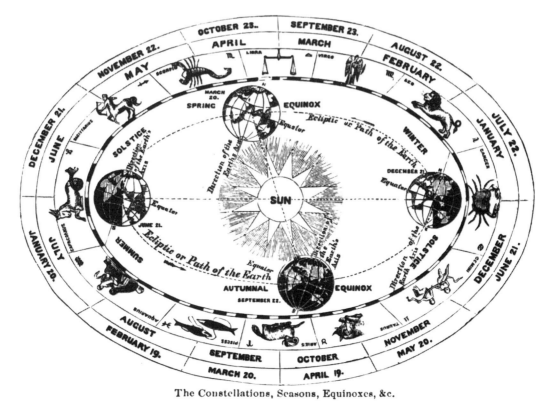

The Constellations, Seasons, Equinoxes, &c.

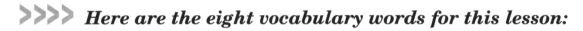

>>>> *Here are the eight vocabulary words for this lesson:*

chart	future	ancient	planets
opportunity	generous	superstition	ambitious

>>>> *There are four blank spaces in the story below. Four vocabulary words have already been used in the story. They are underlined. Use the other four words to fill in the blanks.*

Many people don't believe in astrology. They do not think that one's sign at birth is important. _____ or stars have nothing to do with the kind of person you become. Many scientists think that <u>superstition</u> makes people believe in astrology. But some people jump at the _____ to have their fortunes told. They feel that being <u>ambitious</u> or _____ is all in one's stars. Many <u>ancient</u> people believed in astrology. They made up a _____ of the heavens. Each part is named after a group of stars. These people believed that they could tell the <u>future</u> by reading the stars. Do you believe your sign at birth determines what you are today?

>>>> *On a separate piece of paper or in your notebook or journal, complete one or more of the activities below.*

Broadening Your Understanding

Research the Chinese zodiac. Describe it and then find out what sign you are. Write what characteristics you are supposed to have. Then write about whether your Chinese zodiac sign describes you or not. Share your opinion with your classmates.

Learning Across the Curriculum

Astrology is based on groups of stars called constellations. Research what constellations you might find in the sky above your town or city. Go outside at night and identify as many constellations as you can. Draw and label them.

Broadening Your Understanding

Read a story about the creation of a constellation. Then write your own origin story about a zodiac constellation.

9 ART WITH HEART

Of course, you know the story of Peter Rabbit. But did you know about the **author** of the story, Beatrix Potter? Potter wrote more than 25 other books and gave us many happy memories from our childhoods.

Potter's own childhood, however, was not so happy. She was raised in a wealthy English family at the end of the 1800s. Her parents were busy and rarely saw her. Fortunately, Potter had many pets. She spent her lonely hours drawing and redrawing the animals that she kept in a family "zoo."

Her first book, *The Tale of Peter Rabbit*, was written for a sick child. She printed the book at her own **expense** because book **publishers** told her the book would not sell. Today Potter's books sell about 7 million copies a year. They are also printed in 16 other languages. Potter is one of the most successful authors of all time.

Potter had strong feelings for animals and nature. She believed in the **conservation** of the countryside and its animals and plants. When she died, she **donated** her large sheep farm to the British people. She also left hundreds of careful drawings of mushrooms, leaves, and animals. These drawings are so **realistic** that museums use them today to identify new additions to their collections. Potter's **great** powers of **observation** gave her a love of nature that she handed down to her readers.

MAKE A LIST

>>>> *There are eight vocabulary words in this lesson. In the story, they are boxed in color. Copy the vocabulary words here.*

1._____   5._____

2._____   6._____

3._____   7._____

4._____   8._____

MAKE AN ALPHABETICAL LIST

>>>> *Here are the eight words you copied on the previous page. Write them in alphabetical order in the spaces below.*

author	donated	expense	realistic
publishers	great	conservation	observation

1._____   5._____

2._____   6._____

3._____   7._____

4._____   8._____

WHAT DO THE WORDS MEAN?

>>>> *Following are some meanings, or definitions, for the eight vocabulary words in this lesson. Write the words next to their definitions.*

1. _____ protection; preservation

2. _____ true; correct

3. _____ makers of printed books

4. _____ attention; watching

5. _____ writer

6. _____ gave

7. _____ the cost of something

8. _____ much above average

USE YOUR OWN WORDS

>>>> *Look at the picture. What words come into your mind? Write them on the lines below. To help you get started, here are two good words:*

1. rabbit
2. friendly
3.
4.

5.
6.
7.
8.

>>>> A **synonym** is a word that means the same, or nearly the same, as another word. *Happy* and *glad* are synonyms.

>>>> *The column on the left contains the eight key words in the story. To the right of each key word are three other words or groups of words. Two of these are synonyms for the key word. Circle the two synonyms.*

1. **author**	book creator	book buyer	writer
2. **expense**	cost	loss	price
3. **publishers**	book collectors	makers of books	distributors of books
4. **conservation**	preservation	protection	ownership
5. **donated**	gave	presented	lost
6. **realistic**	accurate	violent	lifelike
7. **great**	superior	outstanding	fortunate
8. **observation**	watching	arguing	looking

>>>> Some words are often confused because they look alike or sound alike. For example, *there/their* and *to/too* are often confused.

>>>> ***Place the correct word in the blank spaces in the following sentences.***

1. **(there, their)** _____ was no way for the Potters to know _____ daughter.

2. **(our, hour)** Potter saw her parents for one _____ a day, which is not like _____ lives today.

3. **(knew, new)** She _____ real happiness whenever she drew a _____ animal or plant.

4. **(pair, pear)** Potter might make a drawing of a fresh, ripe _____ or draw a _____ of family pets.

5. **(maid, made)** The Potters's _____ cleaned her room and _____ the same lunch for Beatrix Potter every day.

6. **(you're, your)** Beatrix Potter might think _____ lucky because you see _____ parents so often.

71

Here are the eight vocabulary words for this lesson:

author	donated	expense	realistic
publishers	great	conservation	observation

>>>> *There are four blank spaces in the story below. Four vocabulary words have already been used in the story. They are underlined. Use the other four words to fill in the blanks.*

Beatrix Potter was the _____ of many children's books. She had <u>great</u> talent. She insisted on _____ details in her stories. Once she complained when another writer had a toad comb its hair. She pointed out that toads don't really have hair.

Although she had to print her first children's book at her own _____, Potter quickly became a popular author. In 1913, she married one of her British <u>publishers</u>. They lived on a farm, trying to protect the natural beauty of the English countryside. They became supporters of <u>conservation</u> projects to protect the land around them.

Beatrix Potter's close _____ of the countryside can be seen in her books. You can find many of the scenes in her books on actual roads around her house. To protect these beautiful places, she <u>donated</u> her land to the British people. It is a museum now, and you can still visit it today.

On a separate piece of paper or in your notebook or journal, complete one or more of the activities below.

Learning Across the Curriculum

Beatrix Potter was known for her realistic drawings of plants and animals. Get several photographs of plants or animals. Using these photos, create a drawing that is as lifelike as possible. Then label the parts of the plant or animal.

Broadening Your Understanding

Check out several of Beatrix Potter's books from the library. Read them and look at the illustrations. Write a paragraph about why you think these books continue to sell millions of copies a year.

Extending Your Reading

Beatrix Potter grew up at the end of the Victorian era in England. The books listed below are about her life. Choose one title. Write what you think it would have been like to live then.

Beatrix Potter, by Elizabeth Buchan
The Country Artist, by David R. Collins

74

Chris Burke is an unusual celebrity. He has never taken acting lessons. Yet, he starred in a television program. He has Down's *syndrome,* a birth *defect.* However, Burke likes to call it "up syndrome."

Burke was born in 1965. His parents were told he would probably never learn to read or write. The doctors *suggested* that they put Burke in an *institution.* Burke's parents did not want to do that with their son. They brought him home instead and gave him lots of love and *attention.* They played games with Burke to help him learn to talk. They played sports with him. They taught him to read.

When Burke was 19, he saw an actor with Down's syndrome on television. He wrote the actor a fan letter. That actor's mother was a television writer. She *mentioned* Burke to the producers of a new television show called "Life Goes On." They were looking for a male with Down's syndrome to play a role in the show. Burke tried out and got the part!

"Life Goes On" showed people what someone with a disability is *capable* of. It showed the *struggle* the family of a disabled person goes through. Most of all, it showed what physically challenged people can do if given the chance!

MAKE A LIST

>>>> *There are eight vocabulary words in this lesson. In the story, they are boxed in color. Copy the vocabulary words here.*

1. _____   5. _____

2. _____   6. _____

3. _____   7. _____

4. _____   8. _____

MAKE AN ALPHABETICAL LIST

>>>> *Here are the eight words you copied on the previous page. Write them in alphabetical order in the spaces below.*

syndrome	struggle	institution	attention
mentioned	suggested	capable	defect

1. _____   5. _____

2. _____   6. _____

3. _____   7. _____

4. _____   8. _____

WHAT DO THE WORDS MEAN?

>>>> *Following are some meanings, or definitions, for the eight vocabulary words in this lesson. Write the words next to their definitions.*

1. _____ group of characteristics, or symptoms, indicating a condition

2. _____ care and thoughtfulness

3. _____ weakness; disability

4. _____ hard work

5. _____ building; housing; an organization

6. _____ able to do

7. _____ spoke about

8. _____ offered for consideration; proposed

USE YOUR OWN WORDS

>>>> *Look at the picture. What words come into your mind? Write them on the lines below. To help you get started, here are two good words:*

1. _____ interested _____   5. _____

2. _____ thoughtful _____   6. _____

3. _____   7. _____

4. _____   8. _____

77

FIND THE SYNONYMS

>>>> A **synonym** is a word that means the same, or nearly the same, as another word. *Happy* and *glad* are synonyms.

>>>> *The column on the left contains the eight key words in the story. To the right of each key word are three other words or groups of words. Two of these are synonyms for the key word. Circle the two synonyms.*

1.	**struggle**	effort	fail	battle
2.	**institution**	organization	doctor	building
3.	**capable**	careless	able to do	skilled
4.	**mentioned**	spoke of	remarked	shouted
5.	**attention**	care	distrust	thoughtfulness
6.	**syndrome**	condition	cure	disorder
7.	**defect**	imperfection	broke	flaw
8.	**suggested**	selected	offered	proposed

USING YOUR LANGUAGE: Nouns

>>>> **Nouns** are words used to name persons (actor), places (city), things (book), actions (acting), ideas (truth), and qualities (honesty). There are two kinds of nouns—*proper* and *common*. **Common nouns** are names of any persons, places, or things: actor, city, condition. **Proper nouns** are names of particular persons, places, or things: Chris Burke, New York City, Down's syndrome.

>>>> *Underline the nouns in each of the sentences below. Place one line under each common noun. Place two lines under each proper noun.*

1. Chris Burke was born in New York City.

2. He has a birth defect called Down's syndrome.

3. Burke starred in the television program "Life Goes On."

4. He played a character named Corky Thatcher.

5. Burke once worked as an elevator operator.

6. Burke went to special schools in New York, Massachusetts, and Pennsylvania.

7. Burke is a role model for physically challenged people.

79

>>>> *Here are the eight vocabulary words for this lesson:*

syndrome	mentioned	defect	struggle
institution	attention	suggested	capable

>>>> *There are four blank spaces in the story below. Four vocabulary words have already been used in the story. They are underlined. Use the other four vocabulary words to fill in the blanks.*

People who have a birth <u>defect</u> want to lead lives that are as normal as possible. This story _____ Down's syndrome, but there are other birth defects as well. Some people who are born with birth defects are _____ of living on their own. They do not need to be put into an <u>institution</u>.

Chris Burke is a disabled person who has become a star. When he was born, doctors _____ to his parents that Burke would never learn to read or write. His parents gave him lots of love and _____. They used games to teach Burke. It was a <u>struggle</u>, but he did learn to read and write. He became something most people dream about—a television star!

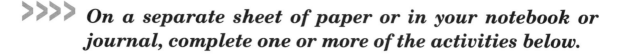

>>>> *On a separate sheet of paper or in your notebook or journal, complete one or more of the activities below.*

Building Language

Learn more about Down's syndrome. Research the subject and write a report about what you learn. In your report, include information about how the birth defect occurs.

Broadening Your Understanding

Imagine you are writing an outline for a television show about a family. One of the people in the family has a disability. Describe the characteristics of the family. Then describe a plot for one of the shows.

Extending Your Reading

There are many kinds of disabilities that people live with. Read one of the following books. Think about one of the disabilities you are reading about. Write what you think a day would be like with that disability. How would your everyday life change?

We Laugh, We Love, We Cry, by Thomas Bergman
The Physically Challenged, by Don Nardo
Disabled People, by Pete Sanders

11 BACKPACKING

Each year, thousands of people go backpacking. Most people hike close to home, and most of them *hike* less than 10 miles each trip. Hikers say backpacking is fun if you are prepared.

First, the hiker must dress *properly.* To start, you will need a comfortable shirt and pants. Boots and two pairs of socks are also needed. Many hikers wear two light sweaters. When you get warm, you can *remove* a sweater. You can put it back on when you stop hiking. This *prevents* the hiker from getting chilled. A wool hat and gloves will also help when it gets chilly.

Next, the hiker must have food and water. Some hikers carry "gorp" in their packs. Gorp is a snack of fruits, seeds, nuts, and candy. It gives the hiker *pep.* Freeze-dried foods are also popular. They come in *compact* packages that are easy to carry. You just have to add boiling water. Minutes later, you have meat, vegetables, and a dessert.

Finally, the smart hiker follows a marked trail. Many hikers also use maps and a *compass.* Many backpackers also hike with a *companion* rather than hiking alone.

How about you? Would you like to try backpacking?

MAKE A LIST

>>>> *There are eight vocabulary words in this lesson. In the story, they are boxed in color. Copy the vocabulary words here.*

1._____   5._____

2._____   6._____

3._____   7._____

4._____   8._____

MAKE AN ALPHABETICAL LIST

>>>> *Here are the eight words you copied on the previous page. Write them in alphabetical order in the spaces below.*

properly	pep	compact	hike
prevents	companion	remove	compass

1. _____ 5. _____

2. _____ 6. _____

3. _____ 7. _____

4. _____ 8. _____

WHAT DO THE WORDS MEAN?

>>>> *Following are some meanings, or definitions, for the eight vocabulary words in this lesson. Write the words next to their definitions.*

1. _____ to take off; to take away

2. _____ an instrument used to tell directions

3. _____ energy; liveliness; spirit

4. _____ to take a long walk or march

5. _____ stops; keeps something from happening

6. _____ correctly; without mistakes

7. _____ a friend; a pal

8. _____ taking up little space; solidly packed

USE YOUR OWN WORDS

>>>> *Look at the picture. What words come into your mind? Write them on the lines below. To help you get started, here are two good words:*

1. _____backpack_____   5. _____

2. _____woods_____   6. _____

3. _____   7. _____

4. _____   8. _____

>>>> A **synonym** is a word that means the same, or nearly the same, as another word. *Happy* and *glad* are synonyms.

>>>> *The column on the left contains the eight key words in the story. To the right of each key word are three other words or groups of words. Two of these are synonyms for the key word. Circle the two synonyms.*

1.	**pep**	energy	dullness	liveliness
2.	**properly**	correctly	without mistakes	thoughtlessly
3.	**companion**	friend	pal	enemy
4.	**remove**	to take on	to take off	to take away
5.	**hike**	to march	to ride	to walk far
6.	**compact**	space saving	loose	solid
7.	**compass**	pointer	something that helps guide you	something that holds packages
8.	**prevents**	stops	packs	keeps from happening

>>>> A **contraction** is a short form of a word or a word group. For example, *can't* is a contraction of *cannot*. *I'll* is a contraction of *I will*. Contractions are formed by putting an apostrophe (') in place of the missing letter or letters.

>>>> *Write the contractions for the underlined words.*

1. A smart hiker <u>does not</u> hike alone. _____

2. <u>It is</u> important to wear the right clothes when hiking. _____

3. Make sure <u>you are</u> wearing two pairs of socks. _____

4. <u>Do not</u> hike on an unfamiliar trail in the winter. _____

5. After hiking a trail in warm weather, <u>you will</u> be ready to hike it in winter. _____

6. I <u>have not</u> had the opportunity to go backpacking. _____

Here are the eight vocabulary words for this lesson:

properly	pep	compact	hike
prevents	companion	remove	compass

>>>> **There are four blank spaces in the story below. Four vocabulary words have already been used in the story. They are underlined. Use the other four words to fill in the blanks.**

Each year, many people strap on a backpack, take a <u>compass</u> in hand, and _____ through the woods. The smart hiker always lets someone know where he or she will be hiking. Many people like to go backpacking with a _____ or two. People hiking together can watch out for one another. They should make sure they rest often. Smart hikers take "snack breaks," too. Eating can restore a hiker's <u>pep</u>.

Backpackers are busy hiking all year long. But when the weather turns cold, some people stop hiking. Other hikers take care to dress _____. They dress in layers that they can <u>remove</u> easily. This <u>prevents</u> the body from getting too hot too fast. A small, _____ pack can carry almost everything a hiker needs.

But remember: Backpacking is not a game. However, it can be fun if you are careful and well-prepared.

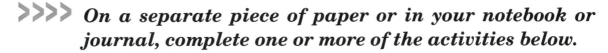
Learn More About Backpacking

>>>> *On a separate piece of paper or in your notebook or journal, complete one or more of the activities below.*

Broadening Your Understanding

Plan a hike to an area that is close to where you live. Research hiking trails in the area. Explain why you chose the trail you did and what someone taking the hike could expect to see.

Learning Across the Curriculum

One of the reasons people backpack is to see plants and animals they do not see every day. Choose a national park and research what plants and animals a backpacker might see on a trip there. Write a description of the plants and animals. If you wish, illustrate your report with photographs or illustrations.

Extending Your Reading

Read one of these books. Then create a list of safety rules for someone who is going on a backpacking trip.

Willy Whitefeather's Outdoor Survival Handbook for Kids, by Willy Whitefeather
Take a Hike!: The Sierra Club's Kid's Guide, by Lynne Foster
Backpacking, by Jimmy Holmes
Backpacking Basics, by John Randolph

12 DOCTOR BILL

Most of us know Bill Cosby as a famous **comic** and actor. His stories of Fat Albert and Weird Harold make us laugh. In the 1990s, Cosby turned his attention to mystery stories in "The Cosby Mysteries." His television program "The Cosby Show" was the most popular show of the 1980s. But Bill Cosby is also a student. He knows the **value** of learning. Even though he finished three years at Temple University, he wanted to learn more. So Cosby returned to school. Between concerts and television shows, he studied at the University of Massachusetts. He was a part-time student for seven years. Then, at age 39, Cosby finally finished school. He **earned** the **degree** of Doctor of Education. This is the highest title given in the field of **education.** It took years of study and hard work to get this degree.

The **path** to success was not easy. Cosby had been a dropout twice. After the tenth grade, he left school to join the Navy. While in the Navy, he took **courses** by mail and received his high school diploma. Later, he left college to go into show business. But he always wanted to **guide** kids. So he combined his ability to make kids laugh with his education. So while kids are laughing with Doctor Bill, they are learning, too!

MAKE A LIST

>>>> *There are eight vocabulary words in this lesson. In the story, they are boxed in color. Copy the vocabulary words here.*

1._____   5._____

2._____   6._____

3._____   7._____

4._____   8._____

MAKE AN ALPHABETICAL LIST

>>>> *Here are the eight words you copied on the previous page. Write them in alphabetical order in the spaces below.*

comic	value	degree	earned
education	path	guide	courses

1. _____

2. _____

3. _____

4. _____

5. _____

6. _____

7. _____

8. _____

WHAT DO THE WORDS MEAN?

>>>> *Following are some meanings, or definitions, for the eight vocabulary words in this lesson. Write the words next to their definitions.*

1. _____ a road or track

2. _____ units of study

3. _____ a paper or diploma showing someone has graduated, usually from college

4. _____ the worth of something

5. _____ gained as a result of hard work

6. _____ a person who makes people laugh; comedian

7. _____ the process of learning; gained knowledge

8. _____ to direct; to show the way

USE YOUR OWN WORDS

>>>> *Look at the picture. What words come into your mind? Write them on the lines below. To help you get started, here are two good words:*

1. _____comic_____   5. _____

2. _____smile_____   6. _____

3. _____   7. _____

4. _____   8. _____

>>>> A **synonym** is a word that means the same, or nearly the same, as another word. *Happy* and *glad* are synonyms.

>>>> *The column on the left contains the eight key words in the story. To the right of each key word are three other words or groups of words. Two of these are synonyms for the key word. Circle the two synonyms.*

1.	**degree**	graduation	diploma	award
2.	**comic**	comedian	student	funny person
3.	**guide**	follow	lead	direct
4.	**path**	road	footprint	track
5.	**education**	learning	building	knowledge
6.	**value**	jewelry	worth	price
7.	**earned**	gained	acquired	lost
8.	**courses**	units of study	classes	grades

>>>> Two of the words used in the story, *path* and *actor*, are **nouns.** Think of your favorite actor/actress and a path you know well. What words can you use to describe them?

>>>> *List as many adjectives as you can that tell something about the nouns below.*

Path	**Actor/Actress**
1._____	1._____
2._____	2._____
3._____	3._____
4._____	4._____
5._____	5._____
6._____	6._____
7._____	7._____
8._____	8._____

>>>> *Here are the eight vocabulary words for this lesson:*

comic	value	degree	earned
education	courses	guide	path

>>>> *There are four blank spaces in the story below. Four vocabulary words have already been used in the story. They are underlined. Use the other four words to fill in the blanks.*

People who can make other people laugh have a special gift. One of these gifted people is Bill Cosby, the <u>comic</u>. But Cosby tries to mix laughter with _____. Cosby's family knows the <u>value</u> of learning. Without it, your chances for success are poor.

Even while in the Navy, Cosby was a student. He <u>earned</u> his high school diploma by taking _____ through the mail. When one has to work and study at the same time, the <u>path</u> to success is not easy. But Cosby kept at it. He became a great success. Yet, there was one more college _____ that Cosby wanted. He wanted to prepare himself to _____ kids. He was concerned about the number of kids who drop out of school. So he studied as a part-time student at the University of Massachusetts for seven years. Finally, he made it. At the age of 39, he could honestly be called Doctor.

>>>> *On a separate sheet of paper or in your notebook or journal, complete one or more of the activities below.*

Appreciating Diversity

Bill Cosby first became famous as a stand-up comic. Jokes are common in every language. Do you know a joke in another language? Translate the joke into English. Then tell it to a friend in English.

Broadening Your Understanding

Learning can be more fun if you can laugh while you learn. The writers of the television show "Sesame Street," on which Bill Cosby has often appeared, understand that. Watch a "Sesame Street" show. Explain how the creators of that show use laughter to teach young children.

Extending Your Reading

Check out a book of jokes from the library. Some books of jokes are listed below. After you have read the book, think about what makes the jokes funny. Write why you think people laugh at jokes.

What's the Score?, by Charles Keller
101 School Jokes, by Sam Schultz
Witcracks, by Alvin Schwartz
Out to Dry: Riddles About Deserts, by June Swanson

The brontosaur had been feeding on plants nearly all day. Suddenly, it heard a noise. An allosaur appeared at the edge of the water. Hooked **claws** buried themselves in the skin of the brontosaur. The brontosaur tried to move into deeper water, but its legs were so heavy that it moved slowly. The allosaur sank its sharp teeth into the backbone of the brontosaur. The brontosaur tried to fight back, but its mouth was small, and its teeth were weak. Finally, the **fatal** battle was over. The allosaur started to feed on the brontosaur. Then it returned to the jungle.

The brontosaur and the allosaur were **dinosaurs.** The brontosaur was one of the largest. The brontosaur was 70 feet long. That is twice as long as most classrooms! Also, this dinosaur weighed about 35 **tons.** It would take ten elephants to weigh as much as one brontosaur!

The allosaur was the **principal** enemy of the brontosaur. Although it was half the size of the brontosaur, it was a **powerful** and skillful hunter. The allosaur **terrified** other dinosaurs.

There are no dinosaurs on earth today. The roar of these **monsters** is gone. However, millions of years ago the land, sea, and sky were filled with dinosaurs.

MAKE A LIST

>>>> *There are eight vocabulary words in this lesson. In the story, they are boxed in color. Copy the vocabulary words here.*

1. _____   5. _____

2. _____   6. _____

3. _____   7. _____

4. _____   8. _____

>>>> *Here are the eight words you copied on the previous page. Write them in alphabetical order in the spaces below.*

fatal	claws	monsters	terrified
dinosaurs	powerful	tons	principal

1. _____   5. _____

2. _____   6. _____

3. _____   7. _____

4. _____   8. _____

WHAT DO THE WORDS MEAN?

>>>> *Following are some meanings, or definitions, for the eight vocabulary words in this lesson. Write the words next to their definitions.*

1. _____ large lizard-like animals that lived millions of years ago

2. _____ main; most important

3. _____ very frightened; scared

4. _____ sharp, curved nails on the foot of an animal or a bird

5. _____ measures of weight each the equal of 2,000 pounds

6. _____ large, scary animals; huge beasts

7. _____ very strong; mighty

8. _____ deadly; causing death

USE YOUR OWN WORDS

>>>> *Look at the picture. What words come into your mind? Write them on the lines below. To help you get started, here are two good words:*

1.   swamp   5. _____

2.   fight   6. _____

3. _____ 7. _____

4. _____ 8. _____

FIND THE SYNONYMS

>>>> A **synonym** is a word that means the same, or nearly the same, as another word. *Happy* and *glad* are synonyms.

>>>> *The column on the left contains the eight key words in the story. To the right of each key word are three other words or groups of words. Two of these are synonyms for the key word. Circle the two synonyms.*

1. **fatal**	deadly	wounded	able to cause death
2. **monsters**	birds	large beasts	huge animals
3. **dinosaurs**	lizard-like creatures	ancient swamps	prehistoric animals
4. **tons**	measures of weight	amounts of 2,000 pounds	measures of height
5. **claws**	hooks	sharp nails	clues
6. **terrified**	friendly	frightened	scared
7. **powerful**	very strong	graceful	mighty
8. **principal**	priceless	main	most important

>>>> An **adjective** is a word that describes or tells about persons, things, or places. The underlined words in the following sentences are adjectives.

The <u>old</u>, <u>green</u> house belongs to the <u>new</u> mayor.

>>>> *Underline the adjectives in the following sentences.*

1. The powerful roar of these tremendous monsters would scare their weak enemies.

2. The deadly battle was over in ten minutes.

3. The allosaur was a clever, skillful hunter.

4. The terrible monster crawled out of the dark, damp swamp.

5. The allosaur had hooked claws and sharp teeth.

6. Although the brontosaur was an immense animal, it had a small mouth.

7. These strange animals lived many centuries ago.

8. With a final roar, the brontosaur retreated to safe territory.

Here are the eight vocabulary words for this lesson:

dinosaurs	claws	monsters	terrified
principal	tons	powerful	fatal

>>>> *There are four blank spaces in the story below. Four vocabulary words have already been used in the story. They are underlined. Use the other four words to fill in the blanks.*

The "Time Machine" can take you back to the age of <u>dinosaurs</u>. You walk carefully through swamplike land. You hear a terrible roar. There, in the center of the jungle, two <u>monsters</u> are fighting for their lives. It will be a _____ battle. Only one can come out alive. You are the first person to see a struggle between a brontosaur and an allosaur. The size of the monsters amazes you. They must weigh many _____. The allosaur is the <u>principal</u> enemy of the brontosaur. It moves quickly. Its _____ dig deeply into the skin of its enemy. Its large teeth grip the neck of the brontosaur. The <u>fatal</u> battle is soon over. The allosaur lifts its head and gives a cry of victory. The other dinosaurs are _____ of the allosaur. They run from the sound of battle. They want no part of this fight.

On a separate piece of paper or in your notebook or journal, complete one or more of the activities below.

Broadening Your Understanding

Research a specific kind of dinosaur that interests you. Then make a model of it. Make your model as realistic as possible. You may want to create a background in which to display your model. Write what the dinosaur ate and where it lived.

Learning Across the Curriculum

Scientists disagree about why dinosaurs became extinct. Research what different scientists believe and what evidence supports their ideas. Use this information to write why you think dinosaurs became extinct.

Extending Your Reading

Read one of these books about dinosaurs. Think about the way you have seen dinosaurs shown in movies and written about in fiction. Write a paragraph about how you think real dinosaurs differ from the way you have seen them in movies or read about them in books.

The News About Dinosaurs, by Patricia Lauber
The Dinosaurs of Jurassic Park, by Wendy Lawson
Living with Dinosaurs, by Patricia Lauber

Or read the book *Dinotopia* and write an adventure or episode of your own. Create a dinosaur you might see and write about it as if you were keeping a daily journal of events.

106

14 WOW! A POWWOW!

What does the word *powwow* mean to you? Many people think of a powwow as a big meeting. To Native Americans, a powwow is a special **gathering.** It is a time to dance and sing. It is a time to celebrate their culture.

People from many different Native American **nations** and tribes come together. The powwow begins with a parade. People in the parade wear **traditional** outfits. Many outfits have **beads** and feathers. Each nation has its own kind of dress.

The parade **leads** to a dance area. Songs are played on a drum. People take turns dancing. Some dances **honor** nature. Other dances tell stories.

One story dance is the jingle-dress dance. It tells the story of a man whose **daughter** was sick. One night the man had a dream. He dreamed of a special dress. The man heard a voice in his dream. It said that his daughter should dance in this dress to get well. The next day, the man made the dress. His daughter wore the dress and danced. Soon she was well!

People who watch the dancing can learn about Native American traditions. They can also learn about Native American customs. Powwows are more than just celebrations. They are a lesson in **history!**

MAKE A LIST

>>>> *There are eight vocabulary words in this lesson. In the story, they are boxed in color. Copy the vocabulary words here.*

1. _____ 5. _____

2. _____ 6. _____

3. _____ 7. _____

4. _____ 8. _____

MAKE AN ALPHABETICAL LIST

>>>> *Here are the eight words you copied on the previous page. Write them in alphabetical order in the spaces below.*

daughter	nations	gathering	leads
history	traditional	honor	beads

1._____ 5._____

2._____ 6._____

3._____ 7._____

4._____ 8._____

WHAT DO THE WORDS MEAN?

>>>> *Following are some meanings, or definitions, for the eight vocabulary words in this lesson. Write the words next to their definitions.*

1. _____ the study of the past

2. _____ to give or show respect

3. _____ handed down by tradition; customary

4. _____ a parent's female child; offspring

5. _____ groups of people with common ancestors and customs

6. _____ a meeting or an assembly

7. _____ guides; directs

8. _____ small, round objects with a hole in the center for a string to pass through

USE YOUR OWN WORDS

>>>> *Look at the picture. What words come into your mind? Write them on the lines below. To help you get started, here are two good words:*

1. _____exciting_____   5._____

2. _____dancers_____   6._____

3. _____   7._____

4. _____   8._____

>>>> A **synonym** is a word that means the same, or nearly the same, as another word. *Happy* and *glad* are synonyms.

>>>> *The column on the left contains the eight key words in the story. To the right of each key word are three other words or groups of words. Two of these are synonyms for the key word. Circle the two synonyms.*

1.	**gathering**	meeting	discussion	assembly
2.	**nations**	groups	companies	people
3.	**traditional**	inherited	customary	garments
4.	**beads**	sweat	round objects	ball-shaped items
5.	**leads**	follows	guides	directs
6.	**daughter**	child	offspring	aunt
7.	**honor**	show admiration	give respect	stuffing
8.	**history**	the news of today	past events	a record of long ago

>>>> *In each of the following sentences, there are words that need capital letters. Rewrite each sentence so the words are correctly capitalized. Remember that capital letters are used in the following places: first word in a sentence; names of people, cars, cities, states, countries; days of the week; months of the year.*

1. modern powwows take place all over the united states and canada.

_____

2. native americans from different nations meet at a powwow.

_____

3. some dancers perform the jingle-dress dance.

_____

4. people watching the dance learn about native american traditions.

_____

5. powwows are a lesson in history for all americans.

_____

>>>> *Here are the eight vocabulary words for this lesson:*

nations	beads	gathering	traditional
honor	daughter	history	leads

>>>> *There are four blank spaces in the story below. Four vocabulary words have already been used in the story. They are underlined. Use the other four words to fill in the blanks.*

A powwow is a _____ of Native Americans. Members of different <u>nations</u> come together. They _____ Americans of long ago. Their <u>traditional</u> outfits are often decorated with _____ and feathers. Every powwow begins with a big parade. The parade <u>leads</u> to a dance area. Some dances are story dances. One story dance is about a man's _____. Story dances teach people about life long ago. They teach people about Native American <u>history</u>.

>>>> *On a separate sheet of paper or in your notebook or journal, complete one or more of the activities below.*

Appreciating Diversity

Draw a picture of a traditional outfit that shows something about your own or another culture. Under the sketch, explain what each part of the outfit means. Name the parts of the outfit in the native language of the country it comes from.

Working Together

Work with a group of students to create a booklet of traditional Native American dress. Describe the clothing of five different tribes in your book. Try to find a photo of each item, or make a sketch. Ask your teacher or the librarian for resources.

Broadening Your Understanding

Use reference materials to learn more about a folk dance from another culture. Find out what the dance means. Then share the meaning with your class.

The people *scramble* to their seats. The show is about to begin! The dolphin's trainer stands high above the water. The dolphin leaps. It grabs a fish from the trainer's hand. Then it *plunges* back into the tank.

Thousands of years ago, the dolphin's ancestors lived on land. Today the dolphin lives in the sea. Dolphins are often confused with porpoises. The dolphin has a pointed noise, mouth, and jaw. The porpoise has a rounded head. The dolphin has a slender, hairless body. The porpoise has a *stocky* body.

Dolphins are *excellent* swimmers. Although they have no back *limbs,* they have strong tails. These tails help dolphins swim as fast as 25 miles an hour.

The dolphin is one of the most *intelligent* animals in the world. Dolphins can imitate actions. They can *memorize,* too. That is how they can be trained to do tricks.

But that isn't all. Dolphins make many clicking and whistling sounds. Some scientists believe that the sounds are a form of language. The echoes of the clicks help dolphins find food. The whistles help dolphins *communicate* with one another. Someday, people may learn how to communicate with these friendly animals.

MAKE A LIST

>>>> *There are eight vocabulary words in this lesson. In the story, they are boxed in color. Copy the vocabulary words here.*

1._____   5._____

2._____   6._____

3._____   7._____

4._____   8._____

MAKE AN ALPHABETICAL LIST

>>>> *Here are the eight words you copied on the previous page. Write them in alphabetical order in the spaces below.*

excellent	memorize	stocky	communicate
plunges	intelligent	limbs	scramble

1. _____   5. _____

2. _____   6. _____

3. _____   7. _____

4. _____   8. _____

WHAT DO THE WORDS MEAN?

>>>> *Following are some meanings, or definitions, for the eight vocabulary words in this lesson. Write the words next to their definitions.*

1. _____   very good; better than others

2. _____   heavily built; thick and strong

3 _____   dives; jumps into

4. _____   arms or legs; parts extending from body

5. _____   to learn by heart; to remember

6. _____   to exchange messages; to give information

7. _____   very bright; having much knowledge

8. _____   rush; move quickly

USE YOUR OWN WORDS

>>>> *Look at the picture. What words come into your mind? Write them on the lines below. To help you get started, here are two good words:*

1. _____ jump _____   5. _____

2. _____ splash _____   6. _____

3. _____   7. _____

4. _____   8. _____

>>>> A **synonym** is a word that means the same, or nearly the same, as another word. *Happy* and *glad* are synonyms.

>>>> *The column on the left contains the eight key words in the story. To the right of each key word are three other words or groups of words. Two of these are synonyms for the key word. Circle the two synonyms.*

1.	**communicate**	to exchange ideas	to talk	to refuse
2.	**limbs**	arms	bodies	legs
3.	**stocky**	short	thick	slim
4.	**scramble**	to rush	to scribble	to move quickly
5.	**plunges**	fills	dives	jumps in
6.	**memorize**	to understand	to remember	to learn by heart
7.	**excellent**	very fine	very good	modest
8.	**intelligent**	smart	pleasant	brainy

>>>> Many words end in *ed, er,* or *ing*. These endings can change the meaning of a word or form a new word.

>>>> *Add the right ending to the word before each sentence. Then write the new word in the blank space. Remember that sometimes you drop the final* **e** *before adding the ending.*

1. **memorize**   The dolphin _____ many new tricks.

2. **scramble**   Alice and Diane were late and _____ to their seats.

3. **plunge**   Several porpoises _____ into the large tank.

4. **train**   She is the best_____ dolphin we have ever had here.

5. **communicate** When the dolphins whistle, they are _____ with one another.

6. **help**   The _____ began to feed the dolphin.

7. **whistle**   Lee thought we could learn to talk to dolphins by _____ and clicking.

8. **perform**   The dolphin is a star _____ .

119

>>>> *Here are the eight vocabulary words for this lesson:*

scramble	intelligent	communicate	memorize
plunges	excellent	stocky	limbs

>>>> *There are four blank spaces in the story below. Four vocabulary words have already been used in the story. They are underlined. Use the other four words to fill in the blanks.*

We are going on vacation next week. Our family has decided to return to Sea World. We want to see the dolphins perform. This time, it might not be so crowded. We won't have to _____ for seats. I hope we won't have to risk our <u>limbs</u> to see the show. The dolphins are our favorites. These <u>intelligent</u> animals seem to know how to _____ with their trainer. They have the ability to <u>memorize</u> many tricks. My favorite is the one trick in which a dolphin _____ into the water and comes up wearing a life preserver.

Some people get dolphins mixed up with porpoises. Both are <u>excellent</u> swimmers, but the porpoise has a _____ body. More important, the dolphin is smarter and seems to enjoy performing. Dolphins are born actors.

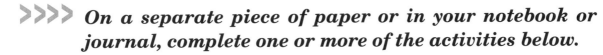

>>>>> *On a separate piece of paper or in your notebook or journal, complete one or more of the activities below.*

Learning Across the Curriculum

In recent years, people have been concerned with the survival of dolphins and porpoises. These people say that dolphins and porpoises are often killed in nets used by those who fish for tuna. The fishers have said that few dolphins are caught in the nets. Research this question and write a report about who you think is right and why.

Broadening Your Understanding

Imagine that you have decided you want a career as a dolphin researcher. Find out more about what dolphin researchers do. Also find out how someone studies for this job. Write a report telling someone the best way to become a dolphin researcher and what he or she might do in the job.

Working Together

Work with a group of three or four students. Together, invent your own communications system. Use sounds or body movements to send simple messages. Share your new language with the class.

A

ambitious *[am BISH us]* wanting fame or success

ancestor *[AN ses tur]* great-grandparent or one who came before

ancient *[AYN shunt]* belonging to times long past; very old

approached *[uh PROHCHD]* worked on; moved toward

attention *[uh TEN shuhn]* care and thoughtfulness

attracted *[uh TRAK ted]* gathered; brought together

author *[AW thur]* writer

B

based *[BAYSD]* centered

beads *[BEEDZ]* small, round objects with a hole in the center for a string to pass through

beat *[BEET]* the rhythm of a piece of music

beneath *[bee NEETH]* underneath, below

brand *[BRAND]* to make a mark on the skin with a hot iron

C

capable *[KAY puh bul]* able to do

chart *[CHAHRT]* a diagram; a map; a graph

chunk *[CHUNGK]* a short, thick piece; good-sized portion

claws *[KLAWZ]* sharp, curved nails on the foot of an animal or a bird

comic *[KOM ik]* a person who makes people laugh; comedian

communicate *[kuh MYOO nuh kayt]* to exchange messages; to give information

compact *[kahm PAKT]* taking up little space; solidly packed

companion *[kum PAN yun]* a friend; a pal

compass *[KUM puhs]* an instrument used to tell directions

confident *[KON fuh dehnt]* having faith or trust in oneself

connection *[kuh NEK shun]* a link

conservation *[kon sur VAY shun]* protection; preservation

continues *[kuhn TIHN yooz]* goes on

courses *[KOHR suhz]* units of study

critical *[KRIT ih kul]* disapproving; not supportive

D

daughter *[DOHT uhr]* a parent's female child; offspring

defect *[DEE fekt]* weakness; disability

degree *[deh GREE]* a paper or diploma showing someone has graduated, usually from college

demonstrated *[DEM un strayt id]* showed; proved

descendants *[dee SEN dunts]* people born of a certain family; heirs

desire *[duh ZYR]* wish; purpose

difficult *[DIF ih kult]* not easy; hard

dinosaurs *[DY nuh sorz]* large lizard-like animals that lived millions of years ago

discover *[dis KUV ur]* to find out; to uncover

display *[dis PLAY]* a demonstration

donated *[DOH nayt id]* gave

driven *[DRIV un]* ambitious; filled with the need to succeed

E

earned *[URND]* gained as a result of hard work

education *[ej yoo KAY shun]* the process of learning; gained knowledge

essence *[ES uns]* basic character

established *[es TAB lisht]* set up; founded

excellent *[EK suh lunt]* very good; better than others
expense *[ek SPENS]* the cost of something

J

jarred *[JAHRD]* shaken; jolted

F

fancy *[FAN see]* fine; elegant
fatal *[FAYT ul]* deadly; causing death
future *[FYOO chur]* a time to come; time that is ahead

L

leads *[LEEDZ]* guides; directs
limbs *[LIMZ]* arms or legs; parts extending from body
literally *[LIT ur ul ee]* actually
local *[LOH kul]* of a small area; regional

G

gathering *[GATH uhr ing]* a meeting or an assembly
generous *[JEN ur us]* willing to share
glacier *[GLAY sheer]* an extremely large mass of ice and snow
great *[GRAYT]* much above average
guide *[GYD]* to direct; to show the way

M

memorize *[MEM uh ryz]* to learn by heart; remember
mentioned *[MEN shund]* spoke about
modern *[MOD urn]* new; up-to-date
monsters *[MON sturz]* large, scary animals; huge beasts

H

N

nations *[NAY shuhnz]* groups of people with common ancestors and customs

hike *[HYK]* to take a long walk or march
history *[HIS tuh ree]* the study of the past
honor *[ON uhr]* to give or show respect
horrible *[HOR uh bul]* terrible; frightful

O

observation *[ob zur VAY shun]* attention; watching
opportunity *[op ur TOO nuh tee]* a chance, usually a good one

I

iceberg *[EYES burg]* a mountain of ice; a large chunk of ice broken off from a glacier
immense *[ih MENS]* huge; very large
informed *[in FORMD]* told; given information
injury *[IN juh ree]* a wound or damage
injustice *[in JUS tis]* something that harms the rights of others
institution *[in stuh TOO shun]* building; housing; an organization
intelligent *[in TEL ih jent]* very bright; having much knowledge
interfere *[in tur FEER]* to get in the way of

P

path *[PATH]* a road or track
pep *[PEP]* energy; liveliness; spirit
perform *[pur FORM]* to do; to act
planets *[PLAN itz]* the nine heavenly bodies that orbit the sun
plunges *[PLUNJ ez]* dives; jumps into
powerful *[POW ur ful]* very strong; mighty
presence *[PREZ uhns]* in the company of

prevents [pre VENTZ] stops; keeps something from happening

principal [PRIN suh pul] main; most important

properly [PROP ur lee] correctly; without mistakes

publishers [PUB lish urz] makers of printed books

Q

quality [KWAHL uh ti] of obvious excellence

quite [KWEYE uht] very

R

realistic [ree uh LIS tik] true, correct

reared [REERD] stood on hind legs; usually done by a horse

remained [ree MAYND] continued without change

remove [ree MOOV] to take off; to take away

reporter [ree POR tur] someone who writes about or tells about the news

reviewers [rih VYOO urz] people who tell about new films, books, plays, or concerts

riot [RY ut] a wild disturbance caused by a group of people

rodeo [ROH dee oh] a public show for the skills of cowboys and cowgirls

S

saddle [SAD ul] a leather seat for a rider on horseback

scramble [SKRAM bul] to rush; to move quickly

separated [SEP uh rayt id] set apart; not together

series [SEER eez] a television show that appears each week

serious [SER ee uhs] sober; sincere

simple [SIHM puhl] plain; common

special [SPESH uhl] different; important

staggering [STAG ur ing] overwhelming

stocky [STOK ee] heavily built; thick and strong

struck [STRUK] hit with a sudden discovery

struggle [STRUG ul] hard work

suggested [suhg JEST uhd] offered for consideration; proposed

superstition [soo pur STISH un] belief based on ignorance and fear

syndrome [SIN drohm] group of characteristics, or symptoms, indicating a condition

T

terrified [TER uh fyd] very frightened; scared

tons [TUNZ] measures of weight (1 ton equals 2,000 pounds)

traced [TRAYSD] followed; tracked

traditional [TRA dish shun ul] handed down by tradition; customary

U

university [yoo nuh VUR suh tee] a school of higher learning; a college

V

value [VAL yoo] the worth of something

visible [VIS uh bul] able to be seen or observed

W

wit [WIT] humor; intelligence